ws7,

CW00858217

Prayers
of a Mouse

Text by M. Angela Toigo
Illustrations by Jules Stauber

BURNS & OATES

First published in Great Britain 1985

The original publication *God and a Mouse: A festival of reflective jubilation,* words by Sister M. Angela Toigo, OSB, illustrated by De Grazia, was published in USA in 1972 by Benedictine Sisters, 3888 Paducah Drive, San Diego, California 92117. Copyright © 1972 Benedictine convent of Perpetual Adoration.

British version copyright © Search Press 1985. Illustrations by Jules Stauber, copyright © Verlag Herder, Freiburg im Breisgau 1983.

ISBN 0 86012 150 X

At first glance this may appear rather simple – but the life of a mouse is not complicated. His whole life is full of traps, yet he bears the world no grudge.

The little mouse speaks to his 'Dear God' about everything that moves him – whether the sun is shining or not. He knows that happiness and sadness are both part of life; and that with either he can turn to God. Perhaps that is why the prayers of this tiny mouse are so full of solace and humour.

Dear God,

*M*y home is a small one,
but the door is always open.
Don't knock,
come straight in!
You are always welcome.

Dear God –
stay with me.

Dear God,

*T*here's a draught on the
floor.
My feet ache.
The cat chases me
all day long.
Why did You give me such a
long tail?
Will I always have to run
in order to live?

Dear God –
hold me in Your hand.

Dear God,

I want to sing a song
for You
but my voice is too weak . . .
You only gave me a squeak.
But I am going to sing
anyway . . .

Dear God —
You are smiling.

Dear God,

I am hungry.
The cheese is good . . . but
it would taste much better
if it were not served
in a trap!

Dear God –
call me to Your table.

Dear God,

The church is quiet.
There is plenty of room
in the pew.
I can see You . . . and You
see me.

Dear God –
we are happy.

Dear God,

*I*t is raining heavily today.
I run into the deep grass
for shelter and fall asleep.
I dream of You.

Dear God –
protect me . . .

Dear God,

I am lonely . . .
Do You have any time to
play with me?
Come, let us run together
in the open fields.

Dear God –
wait for me . . .

Dear God,

The flowers smell nice.
So do the weeds.
Each one has its own place
in the ground to grow.
Beautiful!

Dear God –
plant me in Your heart.

Dear God,

*I*run to the crushed leaves.
It hurts them when they
fall from the trees.
. . . but I try to comfort
them.

Dear God –
heal them before the winter
comes.

20

Dear God,

The world is full of
unhappiness.
The people sigh, and drag
their feet on the pavements.
I hide in the alleyway,
maybe it will be safer
there.
No, . . . I think it is best to
go out and face the world.

Dear God —
give them hope . . .

Dear God,

The birds are having a hard time
finding food today.
I offer them my cheese.
Maybe . . . they will come
and eat it.

Dear God –
feed the hungry.

Dear God,

$\mathcal{T}$he stars are so small.
I want to see them closer.
But You have put them too
high in the sky.

Dear God —
lift me up.

Dear God,

*T*he morning dew is fresh
on my feet.
I help the little violets
open their petals, and
jump up to kiss the
dandelions.
They like it . . .

Dear God –
let all the world enjoy a
'good morning'.

Dear God,

hy do the children flee
when they see me coming?
I want to make friends with
them but they run away.

Dear God –
never let me run away from
what I don't understand.

30

Dear God,

The sun is like a great
big fire in the sky.
It is hot, and the cat is
in a bad temper.
I had best stay at home
today.

Dear God –
give the people some shade.

Dear God,

*T*oday I got lost in the
cornfield.
I was afraid, and cried
amid the giant stalks.
They understood my weakness
and said it was not wrong
to cry.
Sometimes it is better to
cry, than not to cry.

Dear God –
help those who cannot
find themselves.

Dear God,

Food is scarce, yet
I have gathered many crumbs
today.
I will give them to those
who are poorer than me.

Dear God –
the poor are grateful for
help.

36

Dear God,

My heart is pounding.
The people have put out
many traps for me tonight.
They do not want to catch
me alive – but dead!

Dear God –
raise the dead.

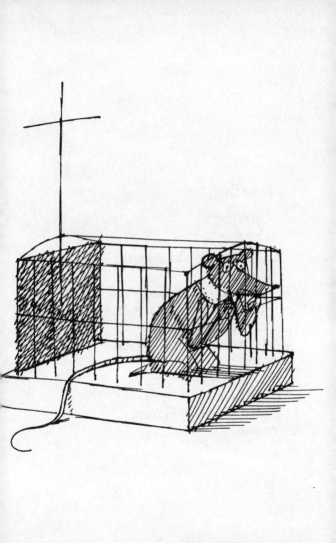

Dear God,

*T*oday the whole world is
laughing.
I can feel the ground shake.
For sheer joy
I try smiling at the cat.
Maybe he will smile back
at me.

Dear God —
turn our enemies into our
friends.

40

Dear God,

I have an important
question.
Cages . . . are they meant to
keep something in or keep
something out?
I look to see if the lock
is on the inside or the
outside.
One day, maybe, nobody will
need cages.

Dear God –
teach the world to see more
clearly.

42

Dear God,

*T*oday I go to a birthday
party.
We will have a good time . . .
sing 'happy birthday' and
give presents.
But why wait until birthdays
to sing songs and give
gifts?
Maybe people need to enjoy
themselves now.

Dear God –
send the invitations.

Dear God,

I am watching the sun go down.
Wonderful!
I clap.
Please do it again for me.
I like watching You.
Maybe tomorrow people will
see lovely colours too.

Dear God –
Show them the sunny side of life.

46